in outer

Sardine in Space
Writer: Emmanuel Guibert
Artist: Joann Sfar
In the far, far reaches of the universe floats the dreaded space prison, Azkatraz . . .
AAARG!

Talk, Yellow Shoulder!
I prefer to scream!

Give him another kiss, space leech!
No, no, no . . .

Are you ready to talk?
No, no, no, I've got a better idea . . .

I'll spit on you and call you names instead!

AAAAARG!
You galactic booger!!

That cursed pirate just won't talk, Supermuscleman . . .
Most unfortunate, Doc Krok. We must find his ship, whatever it takes.

Do you know what's in that ship, Doc Krok?
No, Supermuscleman. He wouldn't reveal a thing.

A ship full of badly behaved children, that's what!

We have trained children throughout the universe to obey us at all times, Doc Krok!
Yes, Supermuscleman.

Yellow Shoulder kidnaps children from our training orphanages and teaches them to disobey!
Disobey? What do you mean, disobey?

Disobedience, Doc Krok, is a major threat to us!
Really, Supermuscle-man?

And of all the disobedient children, SHE is the most dangerous!
Oh! She's so cute!

Is she now, Doc Krok? What's wrong with you?
Oh, excuse me, Supermuscleman! What I meant to say was . . . she's a little galactic booger!

Sardine is Yellow Shoulder's niece. If we get our hands on her, Yellow Shoulder will talk! It's hunting season, Doc Krok!
Yes Sir, Supermuscleman!

Although . . . since her name is Sardine, I should really say "It's fishing season."
Hee hee! Very funny, Supermuscleman.
Jerks!

Now, quick, I've got to find Uncle Yellow!

He must be on one of these monitors . . .

There he is! Poor thing! A giant space leech is about to swallow him whole!

Here's a map of the ship . . . I'm here and Uncle Yellow is there, right near the starport. That gives me an idea!
You Are Here

Change of plans, Yellow Shoulder. We're going after your niece!
Sardine? You'll have to catch her first, you cosmic spitwad!

That's right! Just you try and catch me, Doc Krok!

Swallow her, space leech!
ARGH!
Run, Sardine!!

Here we go!

ARGH!
To the starport!

Phew! That rocket's about to take off!
10...9...8...

...7 ...6 ...5 ...
ARGH!

...4 ...3 ...2 ...1 ..

...Zero!
URGH!
Take that, space leech!

Yay! I got him!
Well done, Sardine!

Uncle Yellow! You escaped by yourself?
Seeing you gave me strength, Sardine. I even knocked ol' Krok!

I was hoping to burn that giant leech, and I figured a rocket would do the job.
If only we had another rocket to get us out of here.

Look over there!
Heave ho, Sardine! We're sailing!

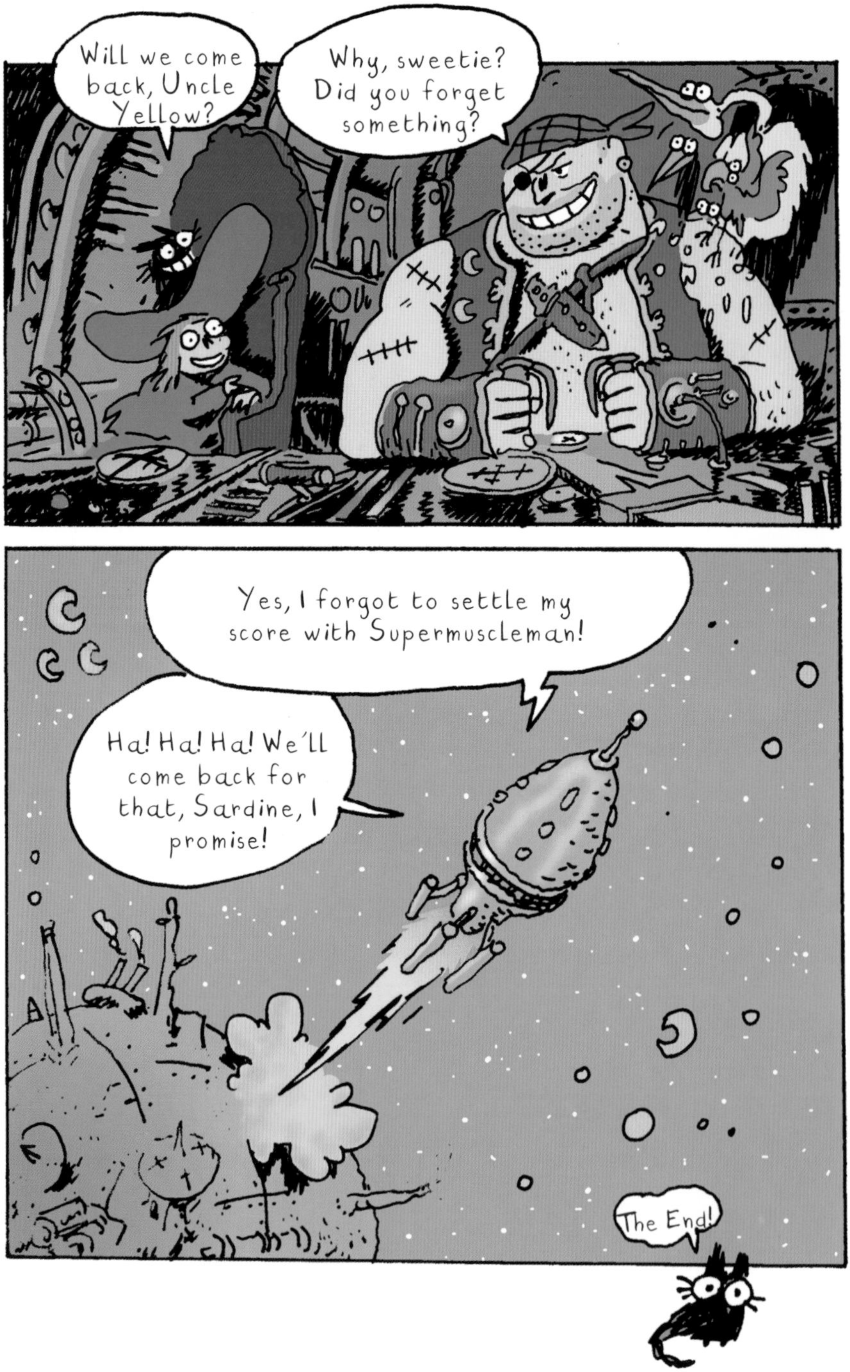

Yes, I forgot to settle my score with Supermuscleman!

Ha! Ha! Ha! We'll come back for that, Sardine, I promise!

The End!

Writer: Emmanuel Guibert
Artist: Joann Sfar
The Electric Lion
Look, Uncle Yellow, there's our spaceship, the Huckleberry.
Yeah! It looks as if it's taken a beating. I hope the kids haven't done anything stupid!

There's no one here to greet us . . . I don't like it!
HUCKLEBERRY

Hey, you guys!!
Anyone here?

Captain Yellow Shoulder . . . is that you?

Little Louie! What in space is going on here?
Oh boy! Nothing good, Captain. We made a big mistake . . .

After you left, we got bored and decided to go check out the constellations of the zodiac!
I told you to wait here for me and not to go out!
On a very warm, beautiful planet, we found a little space lion, and we, um . . . well, we adopted him.
Adopted, my foot! You captured him, didn't you!
And he got a lot bigger after that. He's already eaten four of us! But the real problem is . . .
Yes?

His daddy and all of his zodiac animal friends are after us to get him back!

GRRR
Sardine! You take care of the lion inside the ship, and I'll deal with the one outside!
I'll do my best!

All right! First we've got to dodge these creatures!

Let's try to slip past this bull. He's strong, but not very quick.

OLÉ!

There, I broke through their ranks! Now I've just got to shake them!

That Lion's one mean hunk of metal! He's going to eat us if I don't do something fast!

Yikes!

I'm done for!

Argh!
The daddy Lion is going to eat our ship!
Phew! NO!
He's being attacked by a big dragon!
We've broken into another zodiac constellation! There's a dragon, a monkey, a tiger, and a rat! They're attacking the other monsters!

Nooooo!

Ha! Ha! I'll stick the lion's tail in this outlet! That should calm him down!

Little Louie! Don't do that!!

ROOAARR!

That's just great! You turned him into an electric lion!
I didn't mean to!

How many times has Uncle Yellow told you not to play with electrical outlets!
Well, now what?
GROOOWL!

We have to find some water to short-circuit him
You know Uncle Yellow only drinks space rum!
Space Bathrooms

Jump in the bathtub, Louie!!!
But I don't want to wash!

Fire!
Water!

KRSHTVXZF

Good work, kids! Thanks to you, we're finally getting some use out of this bathtub!

We'll never go out in the constellations of the zodiac again, Captain Yellow Shoulder! I swear it!
Don't make any promises, Little Louie! You never know what the future holds . . .
The End

Writer: Emmanuel Guibert
Artist: Joann Sfar
Total Eclipse
I'm here to give my report, Supermuscleman!
Well, Doc Krok? Have you got news of Yellow Shoulder and his crew of brats?

Yes sirree, Supermuscleman. We have located his ship, the Huckleberry.
Aha! At last!

They're floating in a galaxy crowded full of planets, and now they're heading for a sun. But we've got a surprise in store for them! Hee hee!
What's the surprise, Doc Krok?

A surprise that's good for you and bad for them, Supermuscleman. Hee hee hee!
Yes, but what is it?

But, Supermuscleman, Sir, if I tell you then it won't be a surprise.
If I shoot you in the foot to remind you who's boss here, Doc Krok, then will you tell me?

On Board the Huckleberry . . .
We're approaching the Sun, kids.
YAAAY!

Instead of screaming like space tourists, why don't you put on your dark glasses so you don't go blind?

OK, Uncle Yellow!
Now, look. There it is!

Whoa! I guess you really do go blind if you look directly at the Sun. I can't see a thing!
Neither can I!
But . . . holy space cow! Neither can I!

The Sun went out!

Hee hee hee! I'd like to turn the Sun back on just to see Yellow Shoulder's face right now!
Good work, Doc Krok! So what do we do now that we're in the dark?
Sun On
Sun Off

It's time for the space bat, Supermuscleman!

Go on, Supermuscleman!
Ouch! Don't push, Doc Krok!

Well, you shouldn't have shot yourself in the foot!
Shut up and let's go, you cheeky slug!

With the space bat's super-high-tech equipment, we can fly through the darkness as if it were day. We'll catch Yellow Shoulder in no time. Hee hee hee hee hee!

Captain Yellow Shoulder, I'm scared . . . Can't we get out of here?
We have to go slowly, Little Louie. We're blind as bats and there are asteroids everywhere!

Uncle Yellow, don't you think this seems kind of like a trap?
Could be. A sun going out like a light...I've got a bad feeling about this!

Do you think it could be one of Supermuscleman's tricks?
Him and that vile Doc Krok! Must be.

Here we go!
Clunk!
Click!
WHOAH!

Did we hit an asteroid, Uncle Yellow?
No, swabbie! We're being boarded!

Hands up, Yellow Shoulder! Resistance is futile.
Super-muscleman! Funny, speak of the devil . . .

Put the children in the space bat, Doc Krok. I'll deal with this brigand once and for all.

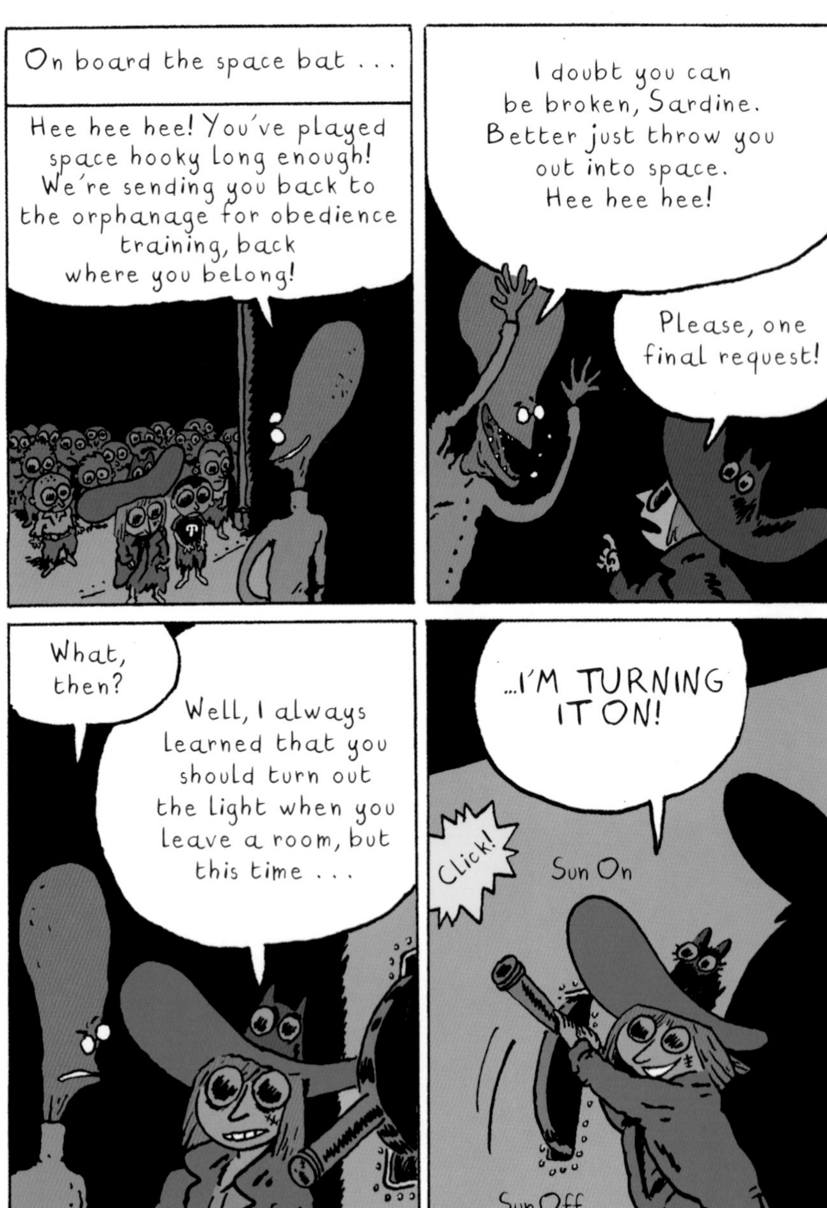
On board the space bat . . .
Hee hee hee! You've played space hooky long enough! We're sending you back to the orphanage for obedience training, back where you belong!
I doubt you can be broken, Sardine. Better just throw you out into space. Hee hee hee!
Please, one final request!
What, then?
Well, I always learned that you should turn out the light when you leave a room, but this time . . .
Sun
...I'M TURNING IT ON!
Click!
Sun On
Sun Off

FLASH!

AAAAH!
BANG!

AAH!

Supermuscleman won't be going anywhere today, Sardine! He shot himself in the left foot!
And Doc Krok got a whopping sunburn, Uncle Yellow!
Sardine did it all, Captain!
Ow ow ow ow!

Well, Supermuscleman? What do you think of my little niece?
GRRR! She's . . . She's . . .

I'll tell you what she is, she's brilliant! DAZZLING!
The End

Writer: Emmanuel Guibert
Artist: Joann Sfar
Honkfish Jamboree
Have a swell time on planet Glug, Supermuscleman and Doc Krok!
GRRR! We'll meet again, Yellow Shoulder!
You too, Sardine!

Glug is an ocean planet made up entirely of water, except for that one desert island . . . They won't get off there anytime soon.
Oh, Uncle Yellow! Can't we go for a swim now that we're here?

A swim? Uh . . . why not?
Great! Little Louie, the last one in is a space clam!

Wheeee!!
Don't go too far from the ship, OK?
SPLASH!

Ha ha! You might be a sardine but I'm an octopus. I'll pull you under with my tentacles!
Just you try it, sea flea!

Wait and see!
FLIP!

Hee hee! Let go of me, Little Louie!

Heeelp . . .

Holy space-a-moly! I don't see the kids!
I never should have let them go swimming!
VRRRRRRR
Over there . . . those shadows heading away from us. Follow them!

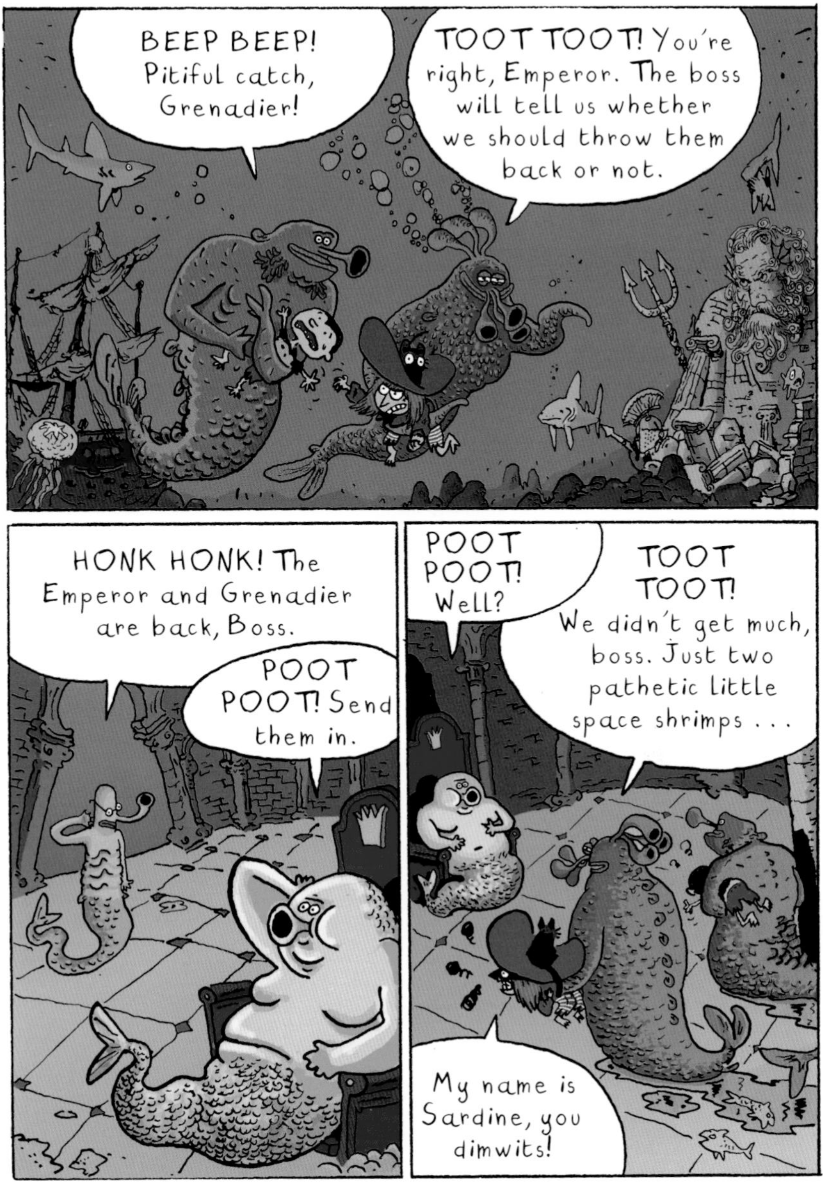

HONK HONK! The Emperor and Grenadier are back, Boss.

POOT POOT! Send them in.

POOT POOT! Well?

TOOT TOOT! We didn't get much, boss. Just two pathetic little space shrimps . . .

My name is Sardine, you dimwits!

POOT POOT! Who are you?
Who are you, you old frozen fillets?

POOT POOT! Ha ha ha! We are Honkfish! And we eat small fry like you, don't we, guys?
BEEP BEEP! Yeah!
TOOT TOOT! Yeah!

But before we eat you . . . POOT POOT! We're going to treat you to a Honkfish jamboree! HA HA HA HA!

POOT POOT TOOT TOOT BEEP BEEP HONK HONK
What is that racket?

OH! Honkfish! They're honking Louie and Sardine to death!
BEEP BEEP TOOT TOOT POOT POOT
Quick, my Honkfish knife!
Charge!
Oops!
HONK HONK! Look Boss! I got a big one!
Holy space macaroni!

POOTPOOT! There's the entrée! Let's eat it raw!
BEEP BEEP! Yeah!
TOOT TOOT! Yeah!
The Honkfish knife!
Poot poot! Dinner is ser-
Surrender, you rotten Honkfish!
Miam!
POOTPOOT! My Honkfish tail!!!

Later . . .
Honkfish are harmless once you cut them in half.
And they make scrumptious fillets!
Can I have some more, Captain?
TOOT TOOT POOT POOT BEEP BEEP HONK HONK
Too bad it didn't shut them up!
I have an idea . . . Let's get the Honkfish out of here!
What are we going to do with them, Sardine?
You'll see . . .
TOOT
BEEP
HONK

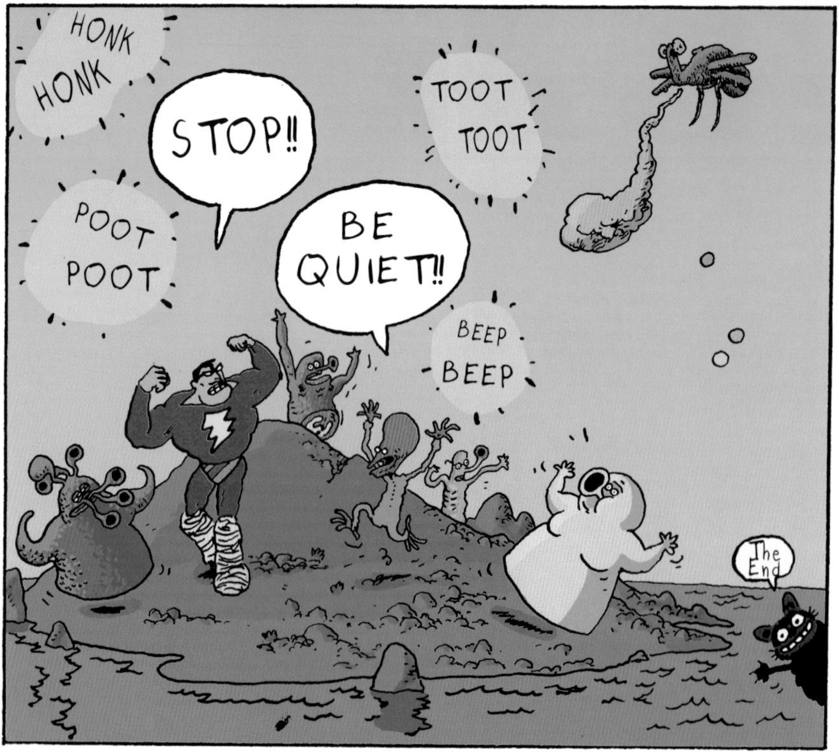

HONK HONK
STOP!!
TOOT TOOT
POOT POOT
BE QUIET!!
BEEP BEEP
The End

Writer: Emmanuel Guibert
Artist: Joann Sfar
A Poke in the Eye
BOO HOO HOO HOO
Uncle Yellow, the alarm!
I hear it, Sardine. Stations!

BOO HOO HOO
Is that a real baby crying?
No! That's the unhappy child detector alarm!

Follow me, Little Louie. We're going inside the FINGER.
Finger? . . . What finger?

When the alarm goes off, a big hand comes out of the rocket, and, at the end of the hand, is the Finger.
Tooot!
Hissss . . .
CREAK . . .
Boom!
Put put put put put . . .

The Finger points us to unhappy children.
But it's rude to point!
It might be rude, but it really works. Hello, Uncle Yellow? Can you hear me?
Yes, Sardine.
There's the little guy. He looks really sad!
BOOOO HOOOO

That . . . that thing is a child?
Not all kids are like us, Little Louie. But we've gotta help them if we can.

Sardine, I'm going down to check things out.
Right, Uncle Yellow!

The Captain is so brave . . .
Nah, it's just his job!
RRzzzzzzzzzzzzzzzzzzzzzz
SOB SOB

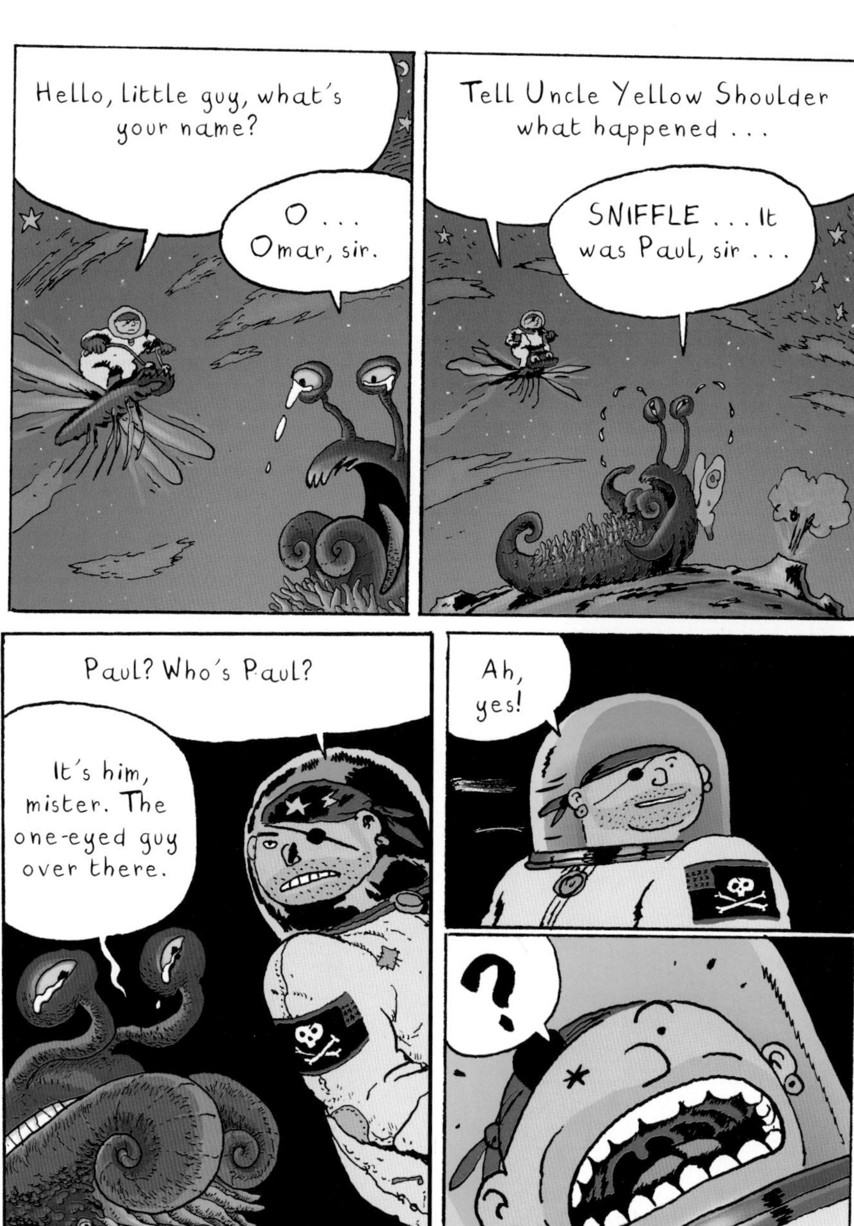
Hello, little guy, what's your name?
O . . . Omar, sir.
Tell Uncle Yellow Shoulder what happened . . .
SNIFFLE . . . It was Paul, sir . . .
Paul? Who's Paul?
It's him, mister. The one-eyed guy over there.
Ah, yes!
?

SNARL!
AAAh!
RRRRZZ
Is the Captain running away?
Of course! He's brave but he's not crazy!

GRR!
SHLOP
SHLOP
This giant's going to catch me!

Luckily, with only one eye, his aim isn't very good!
RRZZZZZZZ

Little Louie, didn't you tell me it was bad manners to point?
Yes, why?

Because we're about to do something that's even worse manners!

Ha ha! I'll crush you, little space critter!
Uh . . . Paul, put that meteorite back where you found it this instant!
Rzt.
Be careful, Louie! Aim carefully!
Eeeeeeeeee!
My eye! My eye!
Nice work, Sardine!

When you said we were going to have bad manners, I thought you wanted to put the finger in his nose!
Eeeeew! Gross!

I think we scared him off. Let's go find Uncle Yellow and the kid.

Omar, that nasty Paul won't be bothering you anymore. Do you want to stay here or come travel through outer space with me and my crew?
Oh, I'm all right here. This is my home.

SPLAATT!

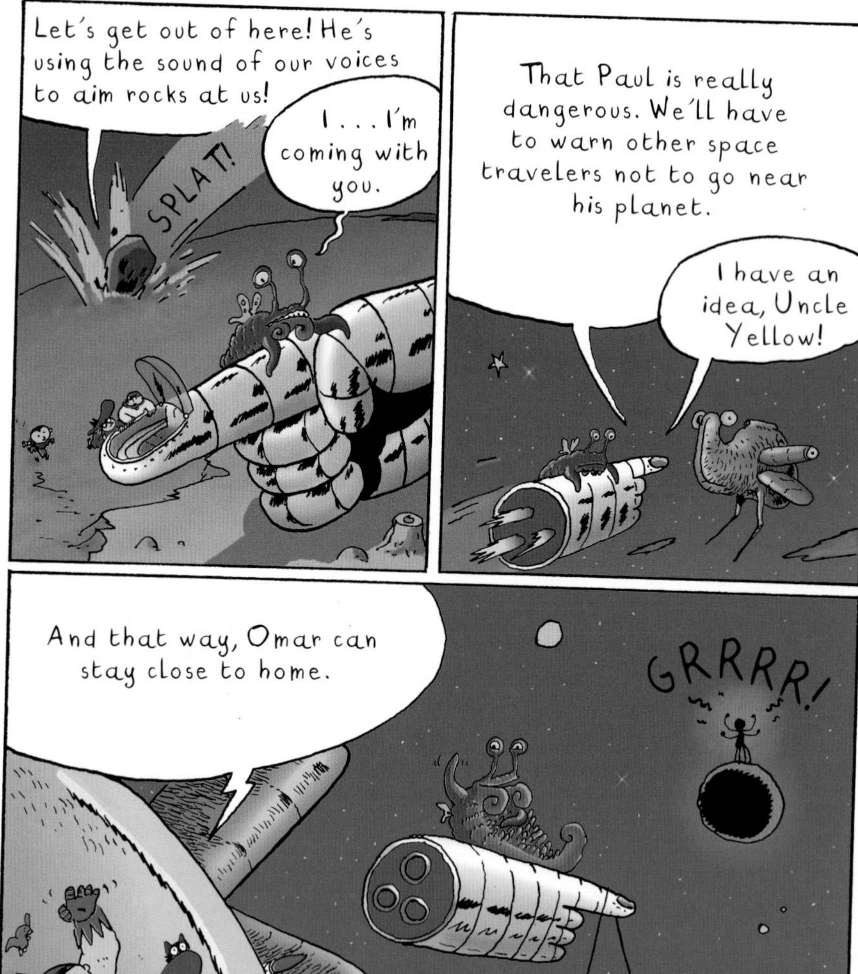
Let's get out of here! He's using the sound of our voices to aim rocks at us!
SPLAT!
I . . . I'm coming with you.
That Paul is really dangerous. We'll have to warn other space travelers not to go near his planet.
I have an idea, Uncle Yellow!
And that way, Omar can stay close to home.
GRRRR!
Warning: Danger
THE END

Writer: Emmanuel Guibert
Artist: Joann Sfar
Planet Discoball
Children, you have to be very good today. We have no choice but to land on the loathsome planet Discoball.
It's funny looking, Uncle Yellow.

FUNNY? It's a loony bin, is what it is!
Why are we stopping here then, Captain?
Because we're out of gas, Little Louie.
. . . And we're not the only ones.
Aw, shoot! There's a line!

HUCKLEBERRY
Hey, you in the ship! How long is the wait?
No one knows. Apparently there's not enough gas.

ATTENTION! ATTENTION! CALLING ALL SHIPS! The Empress Laser Diskette has organized a tournament for this evening. First prize: A full tank of gas. COME ONE COME ALL!

That's easy, Uncle Yellow- we go, we win, we leave.
It's not as simple as that, Sardine. You don't know the great Empress Laser Diskette. She's as cruel as Supermuscleman and Doc Krok combined!
Is she as dumb as them, too?
Ha ha ha! You're right, we'll win her tournament; no problem!

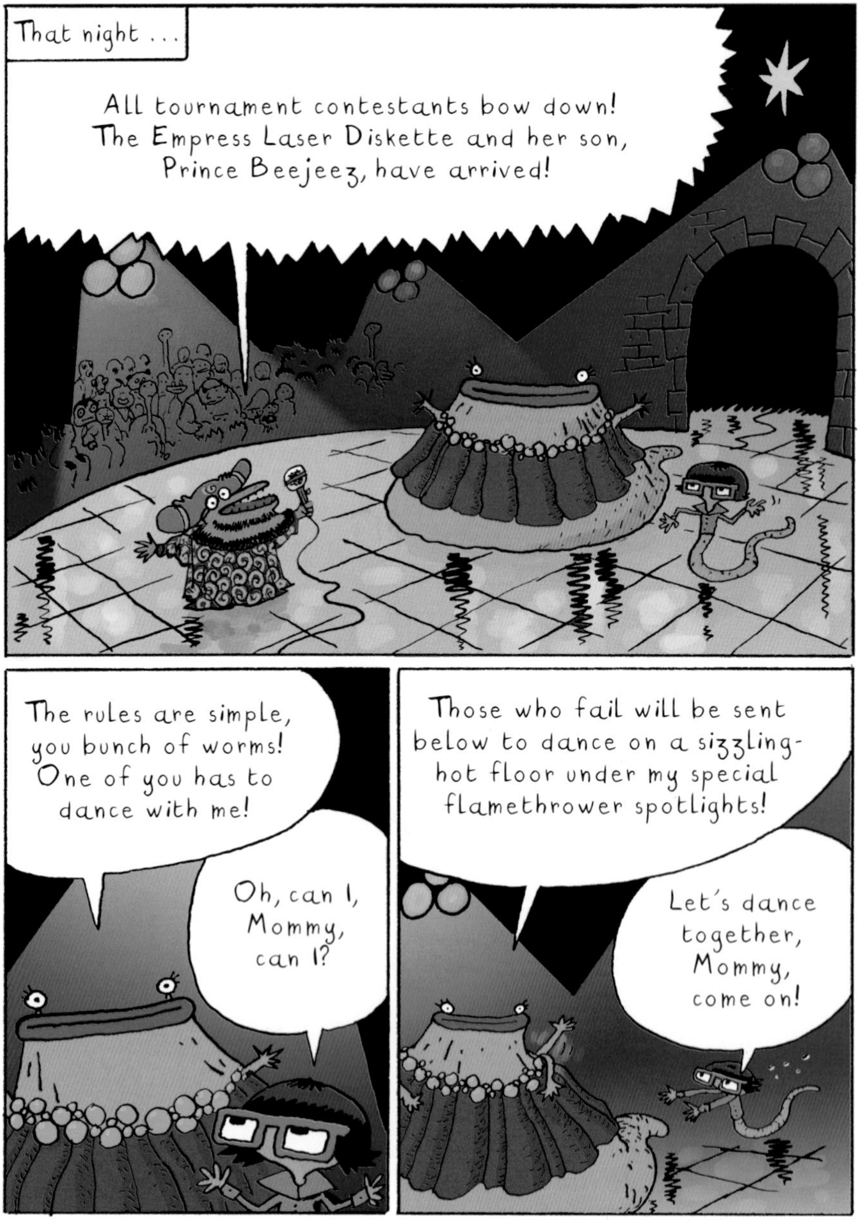

That night . . .

All tournament contestants bow down!
The Empress Laser Diskette and her son,
Prince Beejeez, have arrived!

Those who fail will be sent below to dance on a sizzling-hot floor under my special flamethrower spotlights!

The winner will leave with a full tank of gas and the awesome compilation "LASER DISKETTE PARTY TO THE MAX"!
Bah! I hate this! You never listen to me!

Well, Sardine, I'm not thrilled with this, but I'll do what I've gotta do!
Are you sure, Uncle Yellow? You don't want to wait until she's warmed up?

Come, gentlemen! Who will take the first dance?

Get the gas pump ready, Laser. I am Yellow Shoulder, Captain of the Huckleberry, and I'd like to have this dance.

Start the music, Beejeez! And pump up the volume!
Yes, Mommy.

So, my Captain, do you think you'll win tonight?
Ea . . . Easy!

She's like a mountain, Little Louie! She'll crush him!
He's not moving!

The . . . the music is a little loud, isn't it?
The louder, the better! Are you gonna dance, wet noodle?

She's grabbing him!
She's picking him up!
Ha ha ha! There's one for the barbecue dance floor!
BAAAH!

The Captain gave up without a fight! That's not like him . . .
It's the music, Little Louie. He's too old for this beat. Listen, this is what we're going to do . . .

Do any more of you weaklings want to defend the Huckleberry's honor?
I do!

You, microbe?
Come dance, you big fat space granny! I'm not scared of you!
Boo hoooo! I don't want you to dance with other children! . . .
Don't worry, Beejums. I'll crush this one in seconds flat!
Say your prayers, funny face!
Yo! Yo! Bad boyz in outer space!
Hey you! Prince Beejeez! You want to dance? How about a saber dance!
?

Mommy! The girl with the orange hair is trying to strangle me!!
Surrender, Laser Diskette, and hand Yellow Shoulder over, or I'll do a remix on Prince Beejeez!
My Little Beejums!
Yo! Yo! It's hot, yo!
Later . . .
All right, Empress of my big toe! Fill our tank!
Mommy, Mommy, can I fill it up?
GRRR . . . Be quiet!

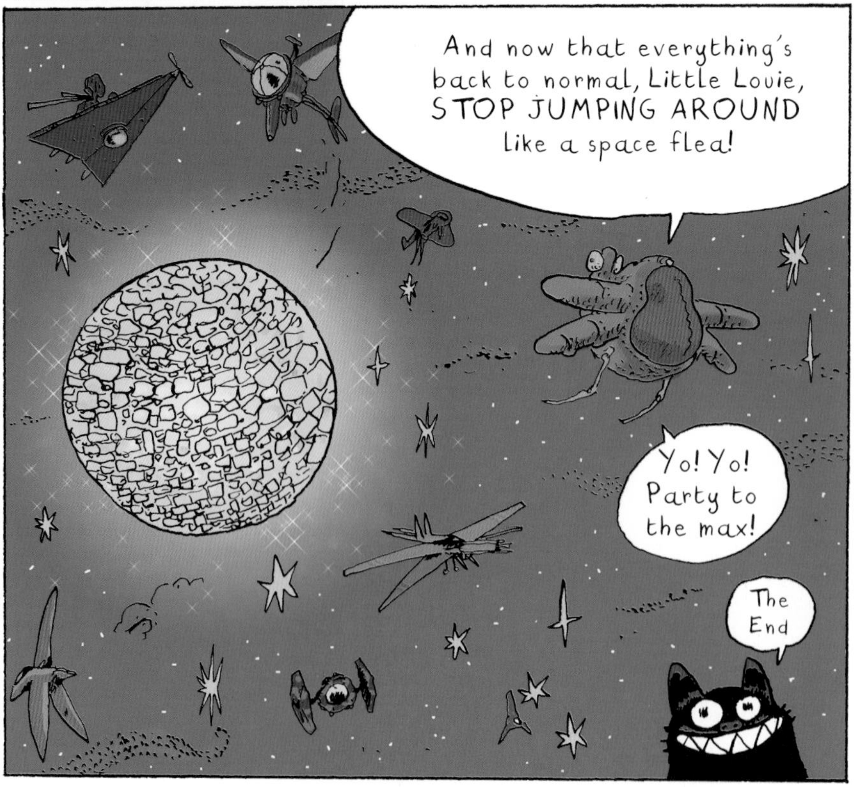

And now that everything's back to normal, Little Louie, STOP JUMPING AROUND like a space flea!

Yo! Yo! Party to the max!

The End

Writer: Emmanuel Guibert
Artist: Joann Sfar
Eating with the Enemy
What'll you have, kids?
I want a solar system!
What's a solar system?

It's an ice cream sundae with a scoop for every planet in the solar system. It's really good!
YUM! I want that too!
And I'll take a space rum.
All right, Captain Yellow Shoulder, honey.
PMU

Well, Krok?
I took their order, Supermuscleman. Two solar systems and a space rum!

Quick, get the spices!
Here they are!

Some leftover noseblow will taste nice on Pluto!
Splotch
Drip drip drip
This eau de baboon will spice up Neptune!
A big glob of mucus is perfect on Uranus!
Plaf plaf
Schlip schlip
On Saturn, a scabby sunburn!
A splash of toilet water is lovely on Jupiter!
Zffft!
Plop! Plop! Plop!
Puked-up lard to flavor Mars!
On Earth, a squishy worm, for what it's worth!
brolobrolo
Shbloop!
Some whipped-up pimple pus is just right on Venus!
On Mercury, some mold that's green and furry!
Blbblblbl
Pshhh
And for the Sun?

For the Sun?
A dash of drippy dung!
Wonderful!
Supermuscleman, it's . . . how shall I put it? Fabulously disgusting!
Ha ha ha! They're going to be so sick!
Yellow Shoulder's rum is poisoned with Yuckamite, an elixir of my own invention that will knock him out cold!
Perfect, Doc Krok! Go and serve it to them now!
What's taking them so long, Uncle Yellow?
It's taking too long, I'm hungry!
Hey! Waitress!
Caw!

Here it is!
Yay!
Yum yum yum!
Finally!

Eat it while it's cold, children! Hee hee hee hee!
Thank you, Ma'am!
How much do I owe you?
Five crollars, Captain Yellow Shoulder.

Hee hee! I'm poisoning him and he's paying for it!
Can we eat?
?

No! Wait a minute!
Wait? . . . But we've been waiting for an hour already!

That waitress said my name twice and I don't know her! That's suspicious!
And this rum smells funny, too...

Don't touch a thing! I'll be right back!
But I'm hungry!
You said that already. Listen to Uncle Yellow.

The bathroom is next door to the kitchen. Maybe I'll hear something if I listen through the wall . . .
WC

Supermuscleman! Yellow Shoulder just went into the bathroom!
Already?
He hasn't even touched his rum yet! And the children aren't eating!
They must suspect something. I have another plan.
Little Louie, Uncle Yellow told you to wait for him!!
Oh, I just want to taste it!
That's strange. I can't hear a thing!

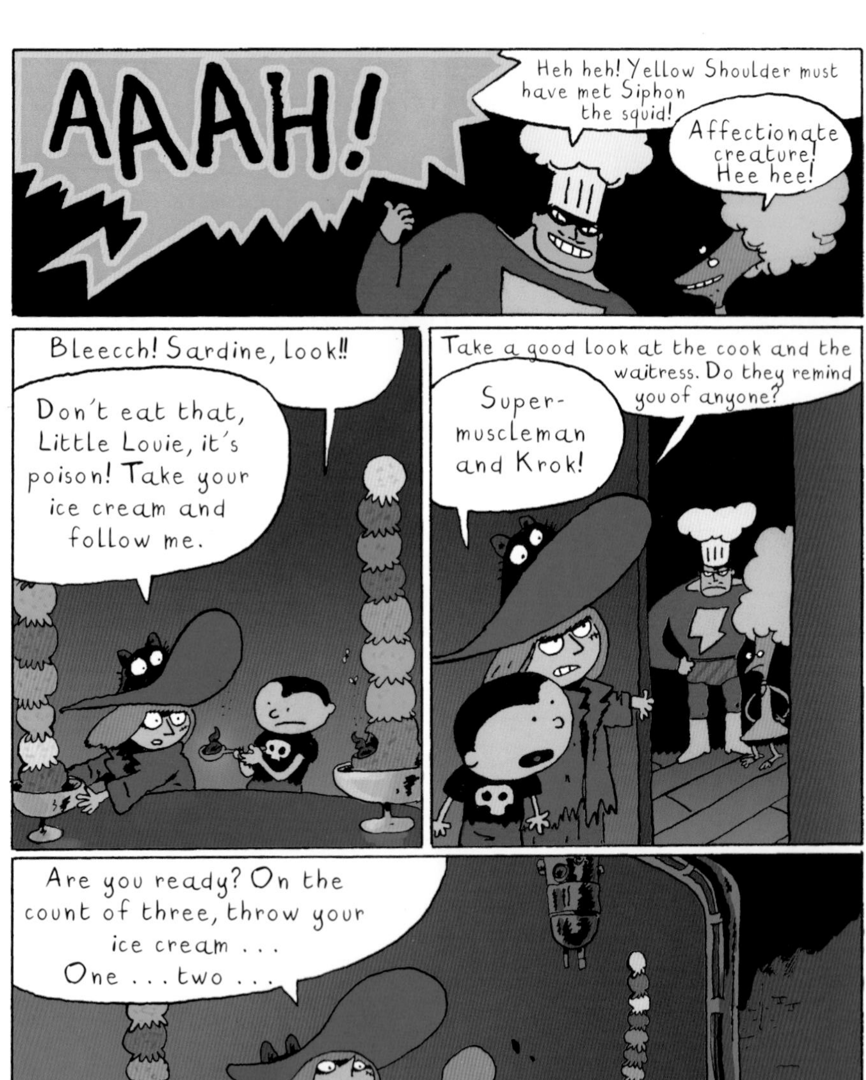
AAAH!
Heh heh! Yellow Shoulder must have met Siphon the squid!
Affectionate creature! Hee hee!
Bleecch! Sardine, look!!
Don't eat that, Little Louie, it's poison! Take your ice cream and follow me.
Take a good look at the cook and the waitress. Do they remind you of anyone?
Super-muscleman and Krok!
Are you ready? On the count of three, throw your ice cream . . .
One . . . two . . .

Three!
Splat!
Splat!

Keep going, Little Louie! I'm going to help Uncle Yellow!
OK!

Uncle Yellow, can I come in?
W·C
TOC
TOC
AAAARGH! HURRY!
Take that, you big squid!!

BLURK!
Get up, Uncle Yellow. There's still fighting to do!
Gg . . .
Don't worry, Sardine! Krok and Supermuscleman finished their dessert and left. They didn't even ask for seconds.
And look, I found some real ice cream! Yum!
Doc Krok . . . I . . . I don't feel very good . . .
M . . . me neither, Supermuscleman...
Well, do something! You're the doctor!
Do something yourself! You're the boss!
THE END

Writer: Emmanuel Guibert
Artist: Joann Sfar
Louie Gets Brawn
What are you doing, Uncle Yellow?
Working on my muscles, Sardine, my muscles!
MOM

Our enemies haven't got brains, but they've got brawn. I have to be strong if I'm going to fight them.
Here, Little Louie! Take this! HA HA HA HA!
Sigh
?
Do you want the body you've always dreamed of? Get it at
HULK AND BULK
the fitness spaceship

Later . . .
Uncle Yellow, Little Louie is gone! And his space bike isn't in the garage!
What? He left the ship without permission?

Look what I found in front of the airlock door.
Oh no! This is serious!

He went to HULK AND BULK. That so-called fitness spaceship belongs to Supermuscleman. Little Louie is in great danger!

Far away, in outer space . . .
Yippee! I'm gonna have big muscles!
HULK AND BULK

Supermuscleman! Come get a look at our newest customer!
Do I know him?
Hee hee! I think so . . .
It's Little Louie!
Yee hee hee . . . and he just walked right into the dragon's lair!
We'll give him a workout he'll never forget, right, Krok?
That's right, Boss!
Open this door or I'll break it down when I'm big and strong!!
Bang
Bang

I want to get big and strong like Captain Yellow Shoulder so that I can punch that dumb Supermuscleman's lights out!

AAAAAH!
SPLOF
Enjoy your dinner, Mr. Louie!
And don't forget to chew every bite! There are some real animals in there!
Captain! Sardine! Help!!

Little Louie is in there somewhere, Sardine!
Charge!

Yellow Shoulder is approaching the ship, Supermuscle-man.
Release Rocky one, two, three, and four!

Robots! Get to your gun, Sardine, and shoot them down!
Right away, Uncle Yellow!

BOP!

SHKLUNK!

BLORPS!
Good work, Sardine! I don't know where that disgusting Liquid is coming from, but it's gumming up all the robots!
BAAAH
FLUBS
I think I hit Supermuscleman's soup tank!
BLLLL
ZLORGZ
Over here!

That's Little Louie!
We've got to get him out of there fast!

This way, Louie! It'll be all right . . .
I wasn't even scared!

And now, let's get even! We're boarding the ship!
Don't wear yourself out, Uncle Yellow!

Look, Supermuscleman and Krok are getting away again!
Those scaredy cats!

Let them take HULK AND BULK! With the time bomb that's waiting for them on board, they won't have long to enjoy it!
Hee hee hee! Ten . . . nine . . . eight . . .
Well, kids, there's nothing more to see here. Let's go!
Look! They blew up HULK AND BULK. They're so dumb! There's no point chasing them or trying to destroy them. They do it all on their own!
Oh, shoot! Little Louie, we forgot to take your space bike!
No problem! I'm not planning on doing any exercise for a while!
THE END

Writer: Emmanuel Guibert
Artist: Joann Sfar
In the Land of the Bully'ems
So, kids, did you pick something out?
Toys
Video Games
TOYS
Yes, Uncle Yellow, we want this!

No-Child-Left-Behind-School II. Isn't that game a little violent?
It sounds great!
It's got lots of new monsters in it!
ASTRO PARKING

Have fun. I'll call you for dinner.
Later, Uncle Yellow!
Come on, let's get our helmets!

Wow! Awesome design!
For our first mission, we have to lug this virtual bookbag survival kit to our P.S. Unit.

Sardine, what's a P.S. Unit?
I think it's that building way over there . . .
All right, let's go!
Louie, watch out!

VROOM!

SPLAT!

You have to be careful! We're not playing the baby level!
Kof! Kof! URGH!
Kof!

We have to cross through this danger zone.
I know what it is! It's a virtual park.

I saw one once when I was little. The green part is called grass and the yellow is sand.
How do we get through?

You take the yellow and I'll take the green!

Shoot, they saw us!
TWEEEET
OFF THE GRASS

TWEEEET
Let's see if I have something in my bookbag that will help me to get away from the virtual park guard!
Yeah!
RIP!
BOOM
Ha ha! I did it! Where's Little Louie?
Hey, Sardine!

That was quicksand over there. I took this little rocket ship from the merry-go-round instead of going through it. Get on!
Good work!
Uh oh . . . the merry-go-round operator isn't too happy...
Take us right to the center of the P.S. Unit, Little Louie.
Whoah! What a mess!

Hey! Look!
New kids!
Let's bully 'em!
Bully 'em!
Bully 'em!
What does bully'em mean?
I think it's the name of their tribe. Don't stop. Go straight in through the window.
More bully'ems!
These ones look more peaceful. Let's land!
You, in the back!
53÷2 =

So, you think this is the right time to come to school?
Well, yeah! We fulfilled our mission! How many points do we get?
You both get ZERO points for being half an hour late!
What?!
Zero points when we got past the park guard, through the quicksand, and past the bully'ems? That's not fair!
Quiet! Go sit down!
I don't get this game! How are we supposed to win points?
Maybe we have to work like all these bully'ems are doing.

Spelling quiz! Take out a piece of paper!
Psst, Sardine, wanna go back outside and fight those other bully'ems?
Shhh! Listen . . .
Dinner, dinner, dinner, dinner . . .
8
Well, this is pretty easy . . .
What a weird spelling test!
Dinner dinner dinner dinner . . .
DIN-NER, DIN . . .
Stop, Little Louie, something's not right here . . .

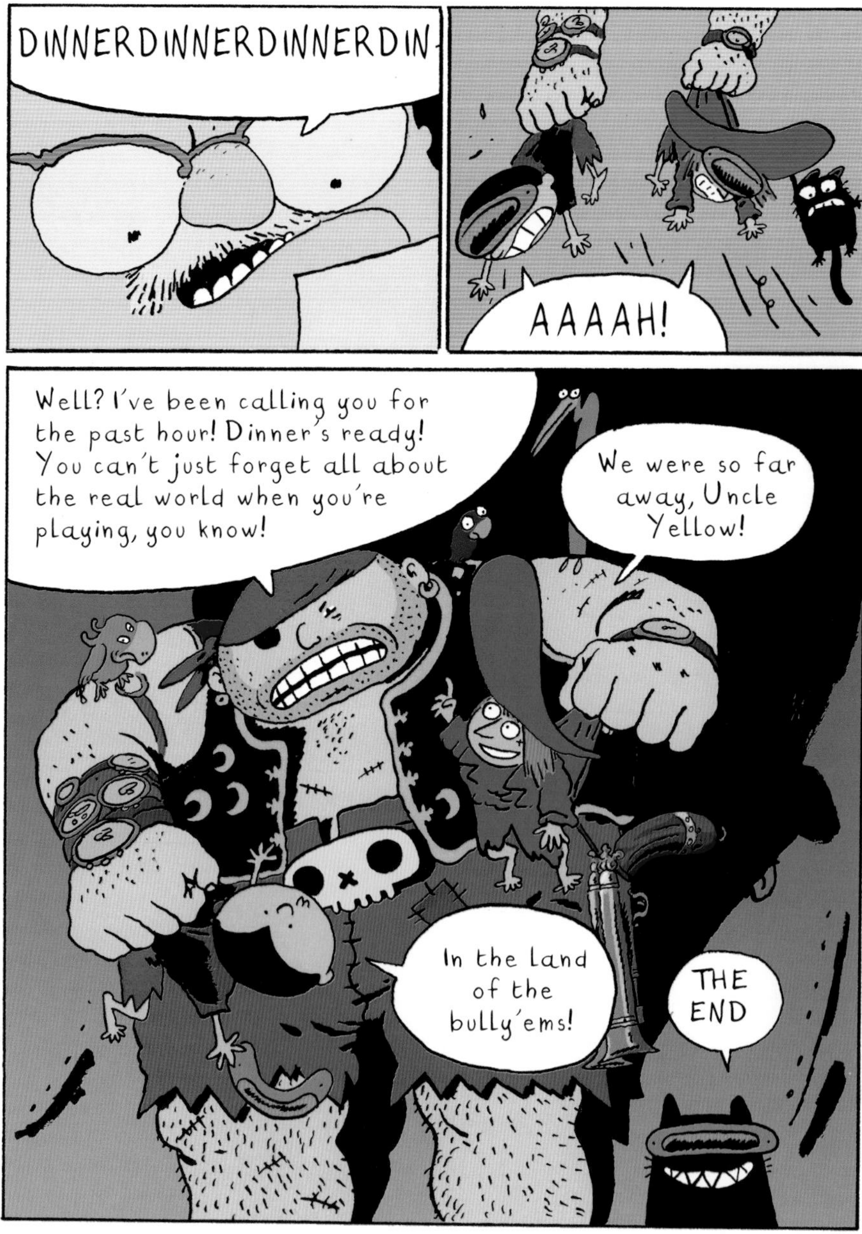

Well? I've been calling you for the past hour! Dinner's ready! You can't just forget all about the real world when you're playing, you know!

We were so far away, Uncle Yellow!

In the land of the bully'ems!

THE END

Writer: Emmanuel Guibert
Artist: Joann Sfar
The New Look
Supermuscleman, you should change your costume.
Oh, really? Why?

That one's old and out of style. You need a new look.
A look?
Yes, a different appearance. Bad guys are supposed to look nice nowadays.
Are you sure about that, Doc Krok?
Think about it! A bad guy who looks bad sends everyone running. Then there's no one to do bad stuff to...
Hmm ...
Whereas a bad guy who looks nice attracts people to him. Especially children. And once he's got them, he can be really, really bad.
Hee hee ... Not a bad idea!
We're heading for the planet Overalls. We'll find something for your new look there!
Planet SALE

At that very moment, on Overalls . . .
So, Sardine, Louie, have you decided?
Just a minute, Uncle Yellow.
Coming, Captain.
DISCOUNT
FINAL SALE
ALL MUST GO
GREAT DEALS
We have to get going. There's a huge crowd and I'm worried we might have trouble taking off.
OK, OK . . . Are you ready, Little Louie?
Yes. Let's go out at the same time.
TADA!
SHAZAM!

My new spacesuit is made out of a mammoth hairpiece. In the winter, it keeps you warm and in the summer, you just take it off!

Yeah, well I've got a COMIXTROOPER outfit that comes with a glue gun!

OK, let's go pay. Are you going to wear your new clothes?
Definitely!
I want to sleep in mine!
PRICES SLASHED

SUPERMUSCLEMAN!

Let's hide, FAST!

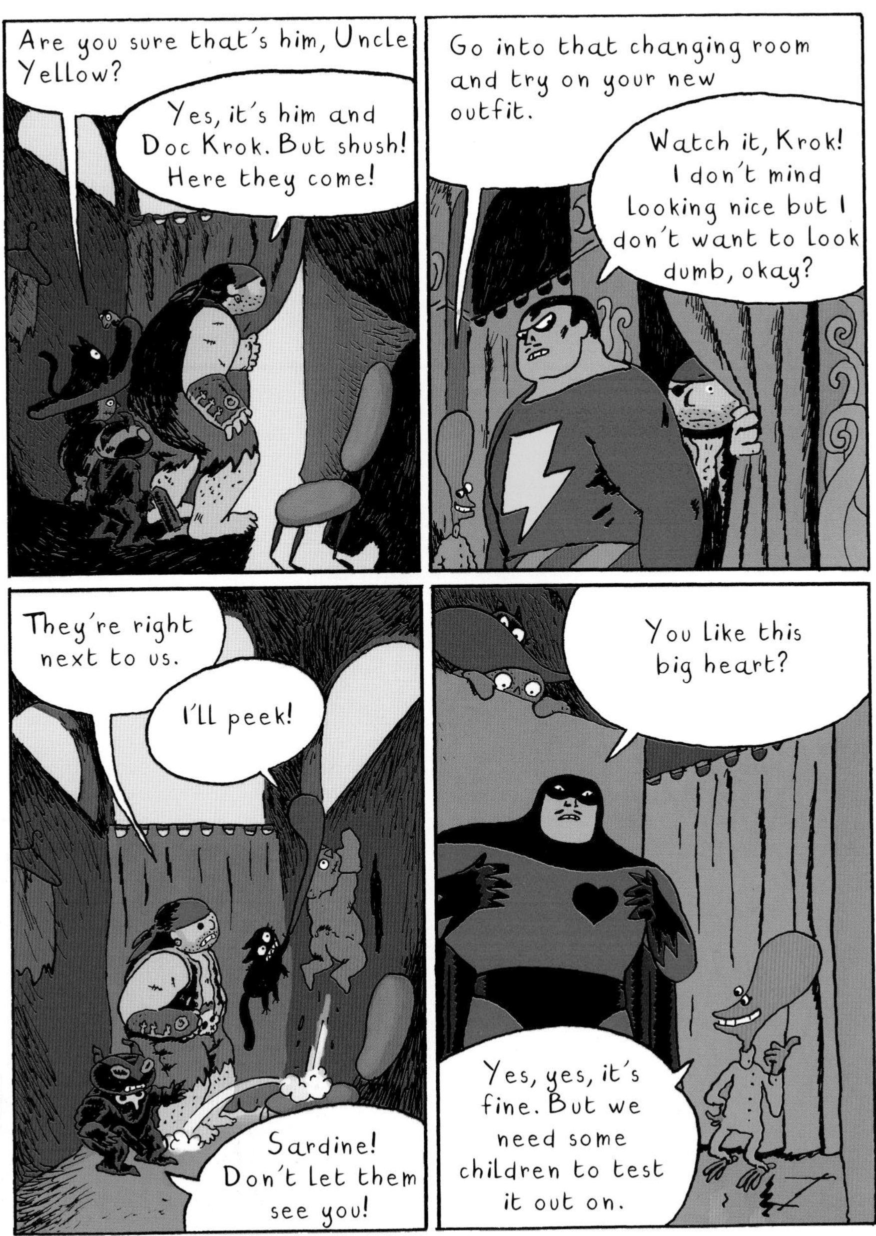
Are you sure that's him, Uncle Yellow?
Yes, it's him and Doc Krok. But shush! Here they come!
Go into that changing room and try on your new outfit.
Watch it, Krok! I don't mind looking nice but I don't want to look dumb, okay?
They're right next to us.
I'll peek!
Sardine! Don't let them see you!
You like this big heart?
Yes, yes, it's fine. But we need some children to test it out on.

What are they doing?
They're trying on ridiculous outfits and looking for children to give them advice. Wanna go, Little Louie?
But they'll recognize us!

Not with our new costumes! Come on, it'll be fun!
Hey, hey, hey!

I'm not letting you go out there alone!
You have to wear a disguise, too!

A little later ...

Ah! Hello, uh . . . Madame. Could I possibly borrow your children for a moment?
What for?
Well, this gentleman here is in need of a little fashion advice . . .
What, he doesn't know how to dress himself?
Tell me, children, do you think I look like a nice guy?
Not really!
I know how you could look a lot nicer...
Oh? How?
Well, there's your mustache . . .

You should cut it!
AAAH!
Snip!
Grow your hair out!
VVOOFF
MMPH...
Wear a nice tie!
KWEEK
GARGL !!
Let some air in!
RIIIIP
Ooph!
Show your butt! It's your greatest asset!
Hey!
They're helpful, eh?

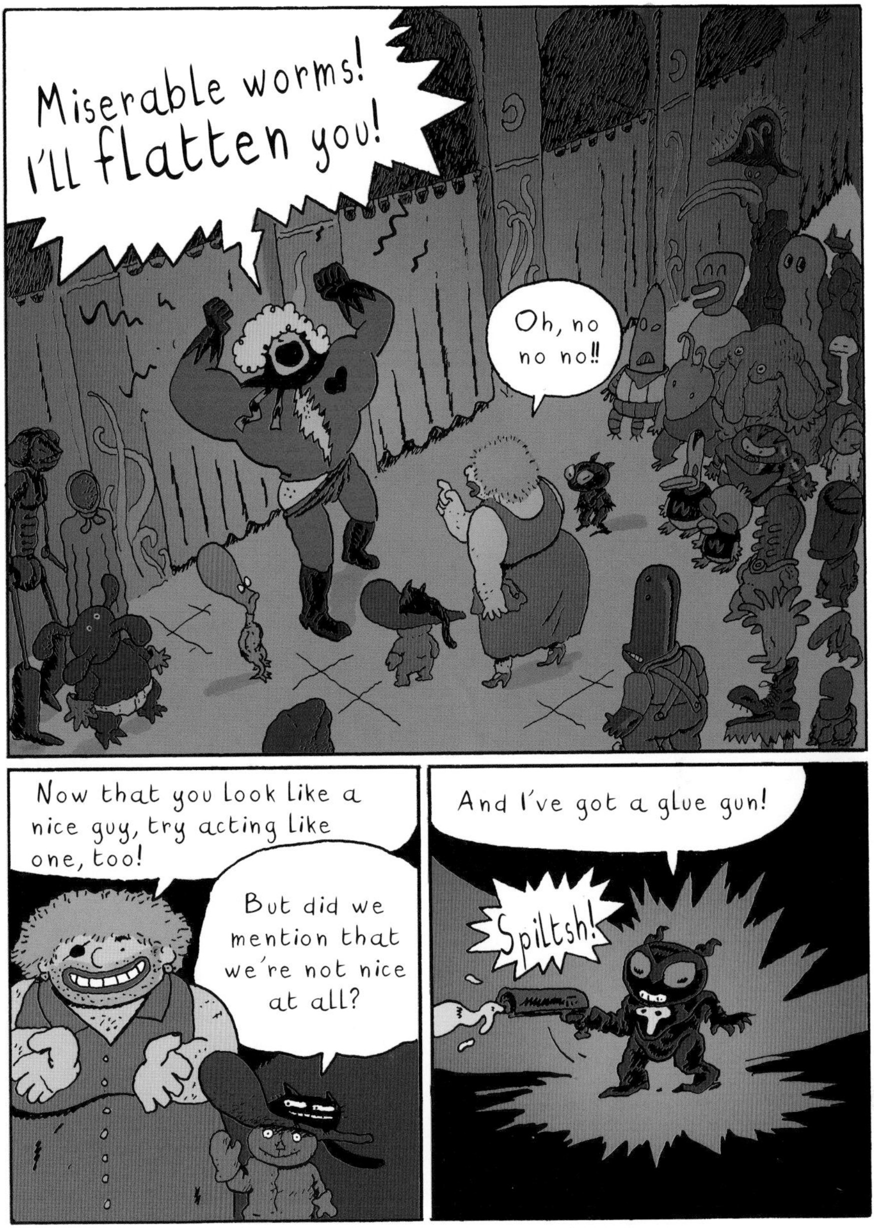

Miserable worms! I'll flatten you!

Oh, no no no!!

Ha! Ha! Ha! We should've taken their picture!
You're the supermodel, Uncle Yellow!
This glue gun is awesome. It's sticking with me!

Doc Krok?
Y ...yes, Supermuscleman?
Now do you understand why I hate children?
THE END

Writer: Emmanuel Guibert
Artist: Joann Sfar
Stratus, Portus, Aramus
Are we going into those clouds, Uncle Yellow?
It's our only chance of getting away from Supermuscleman!

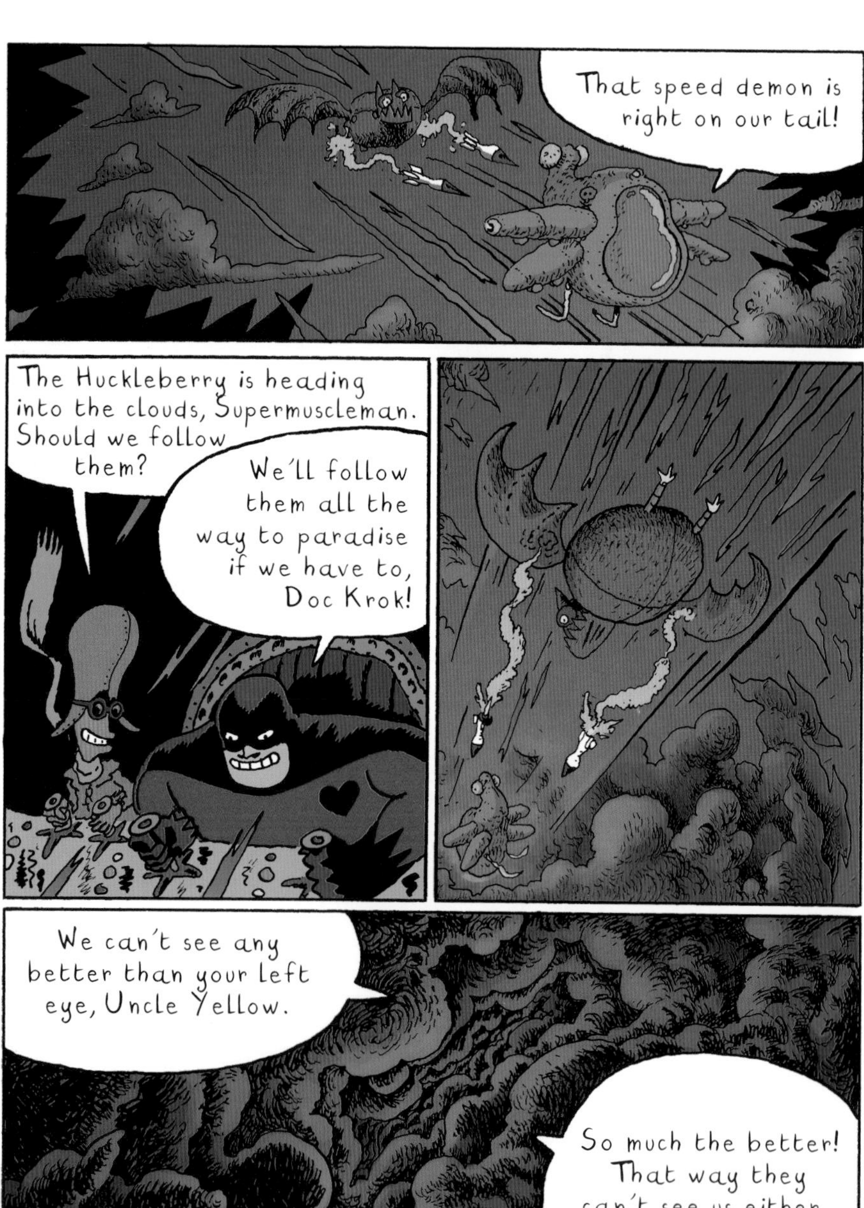
That speed demon is right on our tail!
The Huckleberry is heading into the clouds, Supermuscleman. Should we follow them?
We'll follow them all the way to paradise if we have to, Doc Krok!
We can't see any better than your left eye, Uncle Yellow.
So much the better! That way they can't see us either...

HEY!
BING!
BING!
AAH!
We hit something!
We bounced off it!
Oweee!
Nothing broken, right, kids?
What was that, Captain?

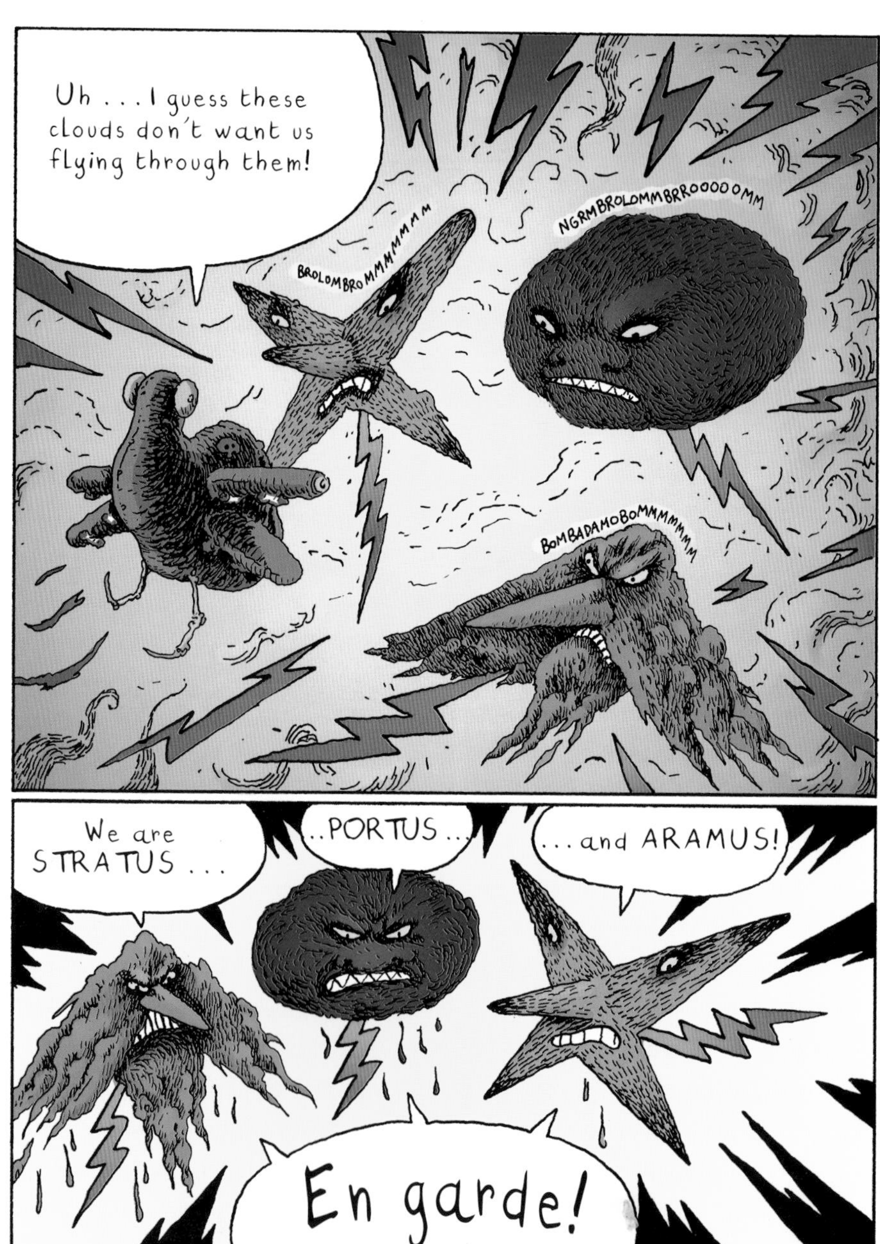
Uh . . . I guess these clouds don't want us flying through them!
BROLOMBROMMMMMMMM
NGRMBROLOMMBRROOOOOOMM
BOMBADAMOBOMMMMMMMM
We are STRATUS . . .
..PORTUS . . .
. . . and ARAMUS!
En garde!

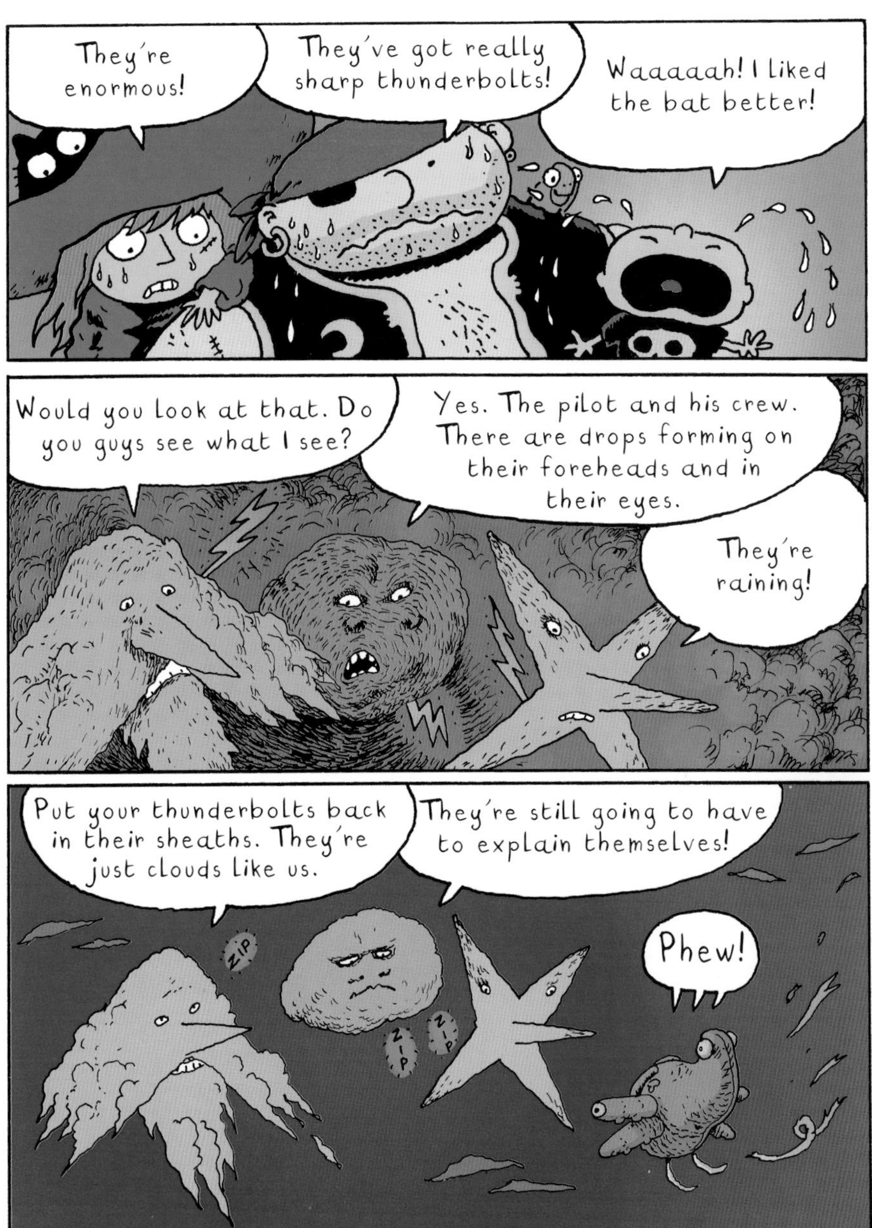
They're enormous!
They've got really sharp thunderbolts!
Waaaaah! I liked the bat better!
Would you look at that. Do you guys see what I see?
Yes. The pilot and his crew. There are drops forming on their foreheads and in their eyes.
They're raining!
Put your thunderbolts back in their sheaths. They're just clouds like us.
They're still going to have to explain themselves!
ZIP
ZIP
ZIP
Phew!

The storm is getting farther away, Uncle Yellow. Stratus, Portus, and Aramus are lightening up.
Let's go talk things over with them!
I hoisted the white flag on a lightning rod, just in case.
Hold it up high, Sardine!
So, little pink clouds, looking for a fight?
We're sorry, great white clouds. We were being chased.
ZZZZZZZZZZZZZZZ

I am a cloud of beer, Portus is a cloud of wine, and Aramus is a cloud of rum. Choose your drink!
Great!
Let's start with a cold beer, kids.
But we don't like beer!
Any soda clouds?
Take a straw and we'll talk . . .
Shh! Just pretend!
Brrrrr
Mmm! It's nice and cold!
It's so chilly and damp here.
ACHOO!

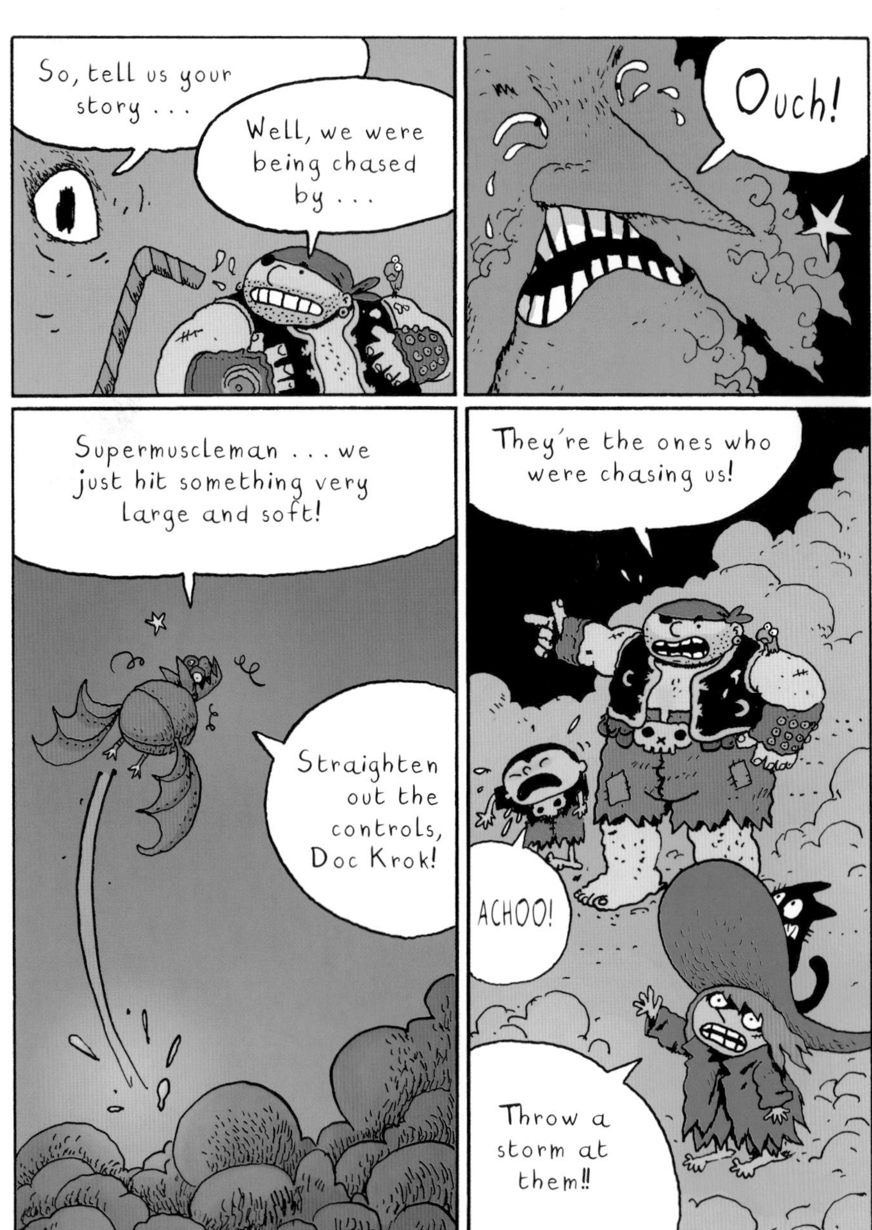
So, tell us your story . . .
Well, we were being chased by . . .
Ouch!
Supermuscleman . . . we just hit something very large and soft!
Straighten out the controls, Doc Krok!
They're the ones who were chasing us!
ACHOO!
Throw a storm at them!!

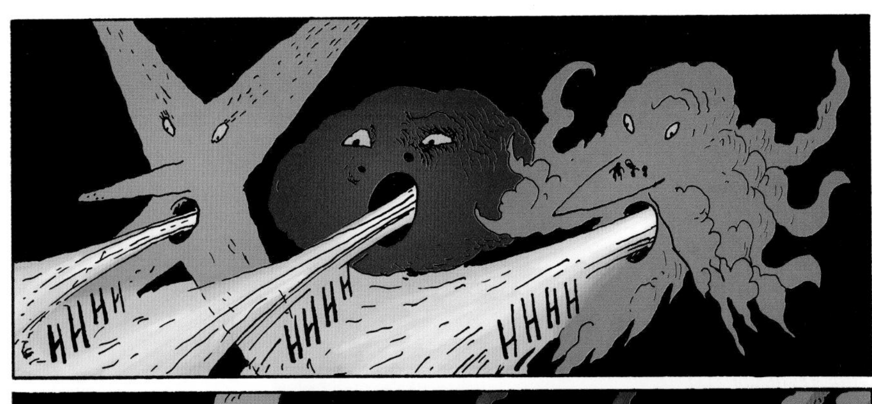
HHHH
HHHH
HHHH

FFFF
FFF
FFF

Straighten us out, Doc Krok!
I caaaaaan't!!

Nice puffing, gentlemen. You blew them away!
All for one and one for all!
Come onto Aramus, Little Louie. He'll make you a grog with his rum!
Splatch!
At the other end of space ...
Tell me, Krok ... We were chasing the Huckleberry and then ... What happened next?
Boo hoo hoo ... An atmospheric depression!
THE END

Writer: Emmanuel Guibert
Artist: Joann Sfar
Pokemon
Hello, hello. Java Blue here. Calling the Huckleberry.
Be CAREFUL when you land, Mom. I'm coming to open up for you.

Grammy's here, kids. Behave.
We will, Pokemon!
Hee hee hee . . .

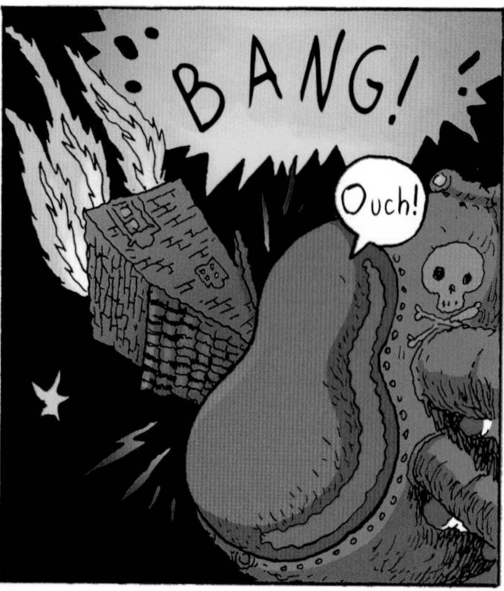
BANG!
Ouch!

My little Pokemon!
Hi, Mom.

I've told you a thousand times to be careful when you pull in. One of these days you'll . . .
Pokemon, these are Mr. and Mrs. SNORE, the old friends I was telling you about.

And this is their daughter, Vinaigrette.
Uhh . . . Welcome to the Huckleberry.
Hi.

GRAMMY !!
My little pumpkinheads! I have presents for you in my rocket ship!

Let's go into the living room. I'm going to make a nice dinner for us.
With French fries, Grammy?

Mom, who are these . . .
Pokemon, if you keep dressing like that, no woman will ever want to marry you.

Like what? I'm dressed like a space pirate!
Look, I brought you a nice warm suit. And it's very elegant, too! Now, put it on.
Mom . . .
And go shave. I want you to make a good impression.
Later . . .
So, how was everything?
Very good!
It's always good when you cook, Grammy!
Can I have some more?

I thought we could go for a nice after-dinner walk on the HONEYMOON. What do you think?
Mom, we can't!
It's far away, it's ugly, and, anyway, I think it's closed.
No, Pokemon, I looked it up. It's right nearby, it's very pretty, and it's always open.
And indeed . . .
Land next to Lake Monamour, Pokemon. Wait till you see how romantic it is!

Why don't you young folks go out for a boat ride! We'll wait here for you.
Yuck! A lake of syrup!

Did you see the Captain? He's acting weird!
I think Grammy wants him to marry Vinaigrette. But he doesn't want to.

What should we do? Should we help him?
Of course, just like we always do!

You know, Vinaigrette, I think you're very nice but . . . I just feel like I'm too young to get married.
That's good.

It is?
Yes, I don't want to marry you. You're always traveling and you've got all these kids following you around. I could never live like that.
We have to turn Vinaigrette off the idea, Little Louie. And to do that, we have to throw her into the syrup.
Torpedo, ready.
Fire!
BZZZT!
?
BOOMM

POKEMON !!
VINAIGRETTE !!

Bull's-eye! Uncle Yellow's gonna be so proud of us!

H . . . HELP! I can't swim in this horrible suit! I'M SINKING!
Come on!

Listen, I'm happy to save your life but don't mention marriage to me again, all right?
ARFEL BLU BLOPS!

I think we messed up, Little Louie. We dunked Uncle Yellow!

Later, on board the Huckleberry . . .
Of course, you had to start blowing things up and causing catastrophes as soon as we get onto the HONEYMOON!
But, Mom, I don't understand . . .
Neither do we, Grammy!
Mr. and Mrs. Snore are very upset. I might as well tell you I was hoping you'd marry their daughter. Fat chance now!
Uh . . . you think?
We did it, Little Louie!
Pokemon, you have to make an effort next time. Promise me that you will!
I promise, Mom.
Good-bye, my little pumpkinheads! Grammy will be back soon!
Bye, Grammy.
Thanks for the French fries.

Sob!
Don't cry, Uncle Yellow . . .
You'll see Grammy again soon.
It's not that . . . Boo hoo hoo . . . It's Vinaigrette . . .
What about Vinaigrette?
I want to marry her!
What in space is wrong with him, Sardine?
Bah! Whenever Grammy comes to visit, Uncle Yellow turns into a big baby . . .
?
Pokemon!
THE END